SUNKEN

Shipwrecks of Lake Superior

by Kathy Groth

Lake Superior Publishing LLC • Duluth, Minnesota

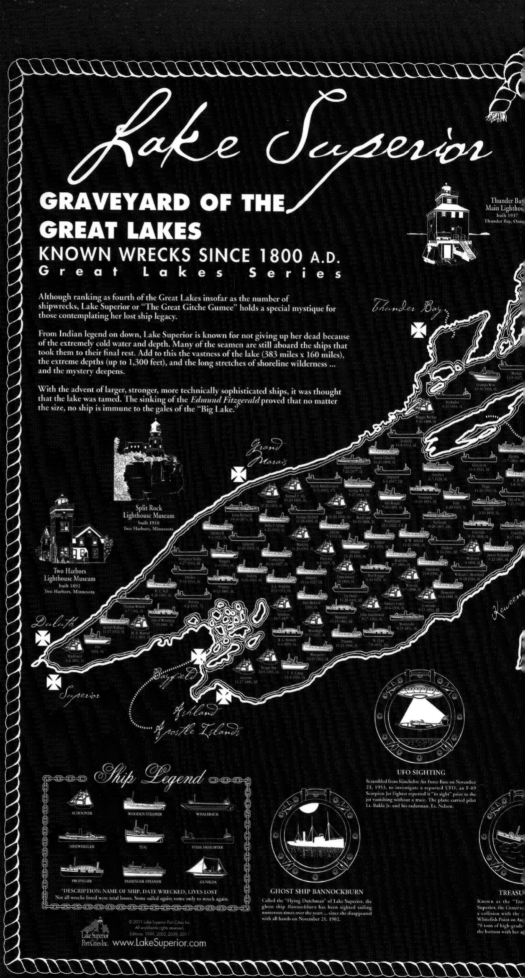

Lake Superior

GRAVEYARD OF THE GREAT LAKES

KNOWN WRECKS SINCE 1800 A.D.
Great Lakes Series

Although ranking as fourth of the Great Lakes insofar as the number of shipwrecks, Lake Superior or "The Great Gitche Gumee" holds a special mystique for those contemplating her lost ship legacy.

From Indian legend on down, Lake Superior is known for not giving up her dead because of the extremely cold water and depth. Many of the seamen are still aboard the ships that took them to their final rest. Add to this the vastness of the lake (383 miles x 160 miles), the extreme depths (up to 1,300 feet), and the long stretches of shoreline wilderness ... and the mystery deepens.

With the advent of larger, stronger, more technically sophisticated ships, it was thought that the lake was tamed. The sinking of the *Edmund Fitzgerald* proved that no matter the size, no ship is immune to the gales of the "Big Lake."

Thunder Bay Main Lighthouse
built 1937
Thunder Bay, Ontario

Split Rock
Lighthouse Museum
built 1910
Two Harbors, Minnesota

Two Harbors
Lighthouse Museum
built 1892
Two Harbors, Minnesota

Thunder Bay

Grand Marais

Duluth

Superior

Bayfield

Ashland

Apostle Islands

Keweenaw

Ship Legend

SCHOONER	WOODEN STEAMER	WHALEBACK
SIDEWHEELER	TUG	STEEL FREIGHTER
PROPELLER	PASSENGER STEAMER	GUNILDA

*DESCRIPTION: NAME OF SHIP, DATE WRECKED, LIVES LOST
Not all wrecks listed were total losses. Some sailed again; some only to wreck again.

UFO SIGHTING

Scrambled from Kincheloe Air Force Base on November 23, 1953, to investigate a reported UFO, an F-89 Scorpion Jet Fighter reported it "in sight" prior to the jet vanishing without a trace. The plane carried pilot Lt. Bakla Jr. and his radarman, Lt. Nelson.

GHOST SHIP BANNOCKBURN

Called the "Flying Dutchman" of Lake Superior, the ghost ship *Bannockburn* has been sighted sailing numerous times over the years ... since she disappeared with all hands on November 21, 1902.

TREASURE

Known as the "Treasure Ship" of Lake Superior, the *Comet* sank in a collision with the *Manitoba* near Whitefish Point on August 26, 1875. 70 tons of high-grade silver ore went to the bottom with her and part of her crew.

FIRST DOCUMENTED SHIPWRECK

The sturdy little schooner, *Invincible*, became the first documented Lake Superior shipwreck on November 14, 1816. She was hurled ashore and dashed to pieces at Whitefish Point in the area to become known as the "Shipwreck Coast." All hands reached shore.

INKERMAN, CERISOLES, SEBASTOPOL

Built for the French Navy at Thunder Bay ... three 143-foot minesweepers set sail on their maiden voyage to France on November 24, 1918. Only the *Sebastopol* made Sault Ste. Marie ... the other two simply vanished with 78 Naval officers and men.

STANNARD ROCK LIGHTHOUSE

Standing in 11 feet of water, 23 miles from Marquette, the nearest land, it is the most remote lighthouse in the world. Erected in 1882, storms have thrown spray over its 102-foot-high dome.

THE GREAT LAKES FISHING TUG

Unique in the world to the Great Lakes, this vessel provides access to a very dangerous occupation, that of Great Lakes fishing. Thousands of men have drowned pursuing the trade by other means. The fully enclosed deck provides a floating workroom from which to set the nets, recover the catch and clean the fish. Greater than that, the enclosed deck allows these stalwart craft to handle the most ferocious storms that the lakes can send to them.

Tying the wheel to a set course allows the entire crew to process the catch while returning to port albeit blind. Sailing thus, the tug, *Razel Brothers*, was run over by a "saltie," sending boat and crew to the bottom in 1986.

THE TALE OF THREE SISTERS

Many seasoned Lake Superior seamen have seen and some survived a phenomenon called "The Three Sisters." The first of three montrous waves running parallel and in unison can knock down even the largest of lake freighters. The successive walls of water give the ship neither the time nor the space to right herself – sending her and her crew to the bottom. Many believe such was the fate of the *Edmund Fitzgerald*.

"Shipwreck Coast"

Whitefish Point

Marquette

Munising

Wawa

Sault Ste. Marie

Sault Ste. Marie

WHITEFISH POINT LIGHTHOUSE

Centered on the "Shipwreck Coast" of Lake Superior, the lighthouse is now home to the Great Lakes Shipwreck Historical Society Museum. Built in 1849, the lighthouse has been restored to duplicate the time that it was actively manned. The large adjacent museum houses many artifacts from Great Lakes shipwrecks, including the Ship's Bell from the *Edmund Fitzgerald*.

THE EDMUND FITZGERALD

The *Edmund Fitzgerald*, renowned in song, is the most famous shipwreck of Lake Superior. She is also the largest shipwreck of the Great Lakes at 730 feet long and the most costly at $24 million. All 29 hands perished as she slipped 530 feet down on November 10, 1975.

Point Iroquois Lighthouse
built 1870
Brimley, Michigan

THE SOO LOCKS

SAULT STE. MARIE (& Visitors Center/Theater) Lake Superior falls 21 feet over a sandstone saddle through boulder-strewn rapids into the St. Marys River, thence to Lake Huron. Ojibway people, French explorers, and later commercial goods and ships were portaged around this barrier.

The first lock was completed in 1855 allowing ships, settlers, and trade to burgeon into the territory to the North and to the West. It opened up vast fields of grain and ranges of iron and copper ore to fuel the nation's growth. Today, more than 12,000 ships a season use the locks with a new larger lock planned.

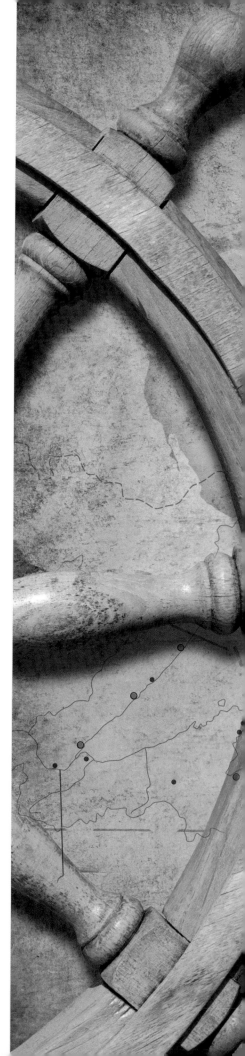

First Edition: June 2021

Lake Superior Publishing LLC.

P.O. Box 16417

Duluth, Minnesota 55816-0417 USA

888-BIG LAKE (888-244-5253)

5 4 3 2

Library of Congress Control Number: 2021937584

ISBN 978-1-938229-56-5

Groth, Kathy 1959-

SUNKEN Shipwrecks of Lake Superior

Storms – Lake Superior

History – Maritime & Great Lakes

Shipwrecks – Lake Superior

Editor: Konnie LeMay

Design: Tanya Bäck, cover & interior; Amy Larsen, production

Cover images: Ship above water by David Schauer; Diver under water (also on last page) by Tamara Thomsen

All internal images used with permission by individuals/ organizations noted (and with our sincere thanks).

Printer: Friesens, printed in Canada

For my grandchildren ...
may you always feel my love
and be inspired by books.

Table of Contents

In Deep Water

Winds howl, drowning out the orders shouted by the captain. Rain hits my face as I scramble along the ship's deck, looking for a safe spot to wait out the storm. Suddenly a huge wave swamps the deck with water. I try to find a railing or line to grab. A second monstrous wave knocks me off my feet. I struggle up and a third wave slams me over the rail and into the icy waters. I sink deeper, deeper into the liquid darkness ...

"Chase! Chase!"

I bolt up in my bed, confused.

"Your breakfast is going to get cold!" Mom warns.

I hustle into the kitchen, my nightmare quickly forgotten as I remember I'm going to travel with Dad around the Great Lakes this summer. We'll tour maritime museums, where Dad will retell his diving adventures and the stories of shipwrecks he's studied as an underwater archaeologist and a member of the Great Lakes Shipwreck Preservation Society.

Dad keeps asking me to dive with him, but I'm never going into water where I can't see the bottom. I am too embarrassed to tell him I'm afraid of deep water.

I gobble down my eggs and toast, give Mom a big hug (Dad does, too) and we head north toward Lake Superior.

In the car, I ask Dad about Lake Superior and the Great Lakes.

"What do you want to know?" he asks.

"How old are they? How big are they? How many of them are there? How ..."

"Whoa, whoa, whoa!" he laughs at my overflowing questions. "I'll give you the short notes:

"The Great Lakes formed over 10,000 years ago, when gigantic glaciers melted, leaving behind 6 quadrillion gallons of water that filled low spots in North America and formed the Great Lakes – Superior, Huron, Michigan, Erie and Ontario. Although it's now the 'Head of the Lakes,' Lake Superior may have been one of the last to fill with water as the glaciers retreated north."

I try to imagine how long ago that was. Were there dinosaurs then? I wonder to myself.

For a minute, my mind drifts into those dark waters from my nightmare, but Dad's words reel me back.

"About 350 ships remain sunken in the Big Lake, the nickname for Lake Superior, which is the largest freshwater lake in the world by how much area it covers – as many square miles as the states of Vermont, Massachusetts, Connecticut and New Hampshire combined!"

I think about how huge Lake Superior is, and I float off on an imaginary sailing ship - in calm water - as the miles flow under the car.

The next thing I know, Dad says, "We're here!"

He pulls into the parking lot near the Lake Superior Maritime Visitor Center in Duluth,

Duluth

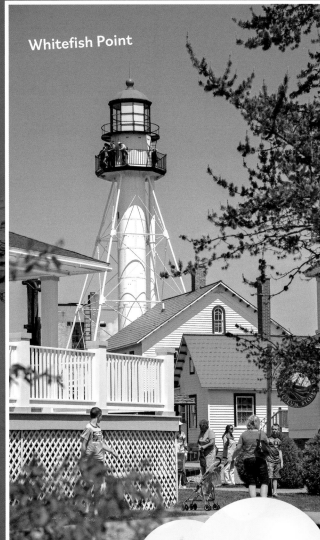
Whitefish Point

Marquette

Did you know?

More than 350 shipwrecks remain within the depths of Lake Superior!

Minnesota, and I see the Aerial Lift Bridge. Waves slam against the piers that run from the bridge to two lighthouses out in the lake.

We carry Dad's projector, books and notes into the center, and I help him set up. As people start coming into the lecture hall, Dad suggests I wander around the museum while he gives his talk.

On the walls of the entry hall hang pictures of vessels that have sailed on Lake Superior plus nameplates and other ship artifacts.

"Wow, these are amazing!" I say out loud, though nobody is in the hallway.

"This is one of my favorites," suddenly comes a voice right beside me. I jump back, startled to find a girl about my age with wild hair that she's trying to tame with a pony tail. She is wearing a short white sundress with a gold belt and golden sandals. I snap out of my stare when she looks up from an old picture of a wooden three-masted sailing schooner. After a moment, she introduces herself.

"I'm Brizo, but most people call me Bri."

"I'm Chase." I say. For some reason I'm tongue-tied, so I look back at the schooner in the picture and don't say anything more.

Breaking the silence, she says, "I heard you admiring these pictures."

"Yah, I love learning about ships," I say.

"Me, too. I come here all the time. I just can't get enough of these boats and their histories."

"Do you have a favorite?" I ask.

"Really, I love them all. But when I come to a maritime museum, I like to start with the early schooners to remind myself how shipping and shipbuilding began. Follow me." ⚓

This drawing shows what the *May Flower* might have looked like based on a photo of the *Dan Hayes*.

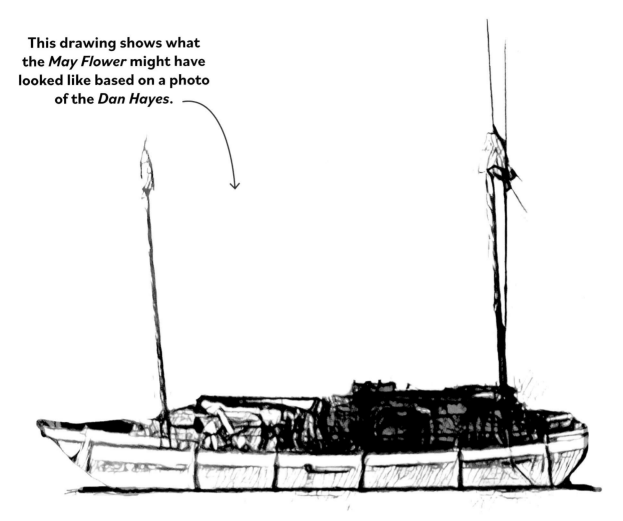

May Flower

In front of us, a drawing with a note card gives a boat name: *May Flower*.

"This doesn't look like the *Mayflower* that brought the pilgrims over," I say.

"That was a different *May Flower*," laughs Bri. "This *May Flower* was 147 feet long and one of the early wooden schooners that sailed on Lake Superior. On June 2, 1891, *May Flower* was carrying sandstone blocks from Portage, Michigan, to Duluth, Minnesota. Back in those days, even though these schooners could sail on their own, they were often towed as barges by other ships. This day the *May Flower* was under its own sail. The weather was good with a wind from the northwest. Approaching Duluth, the captain ordered the sails lowered, but soon after, the cargo shifted and caused the *May Flower* to roll over. It filled with water and sank. Three sailors were rescued, but the captain drowned when he couldn't hold onto the lifeline thrown to him. The *May Flower* was just 4 miles from Duluth's harbor and still lies there today in 90 feet of water."

I'm impressed. Bri seems to know as much as my dad. "How do you know so much about this *May Flower*?"

"Oh, I know a lot about all the shipwrecks," Bri smiles shyly. "It's kind of my thing."

"Will you teach me?" I ask.

"Sure, that would be fun!"

Bri looks around to see if anyone is watching. Then she whispers, "I know a secret about this place if you are up for an adventure."

"I'm always up for an adventure!" I say boldly, but think to myself "as long as it isn't in deep water."

Bri takes me to a dark map called "Lake Superior: Graveyard of the Great Lakes."

I study the map to figure out its secret. Looks like a piece of paper with a lot of little shipwrecks on it to me.

"I don't get it," I blurt out. "What's the secret?"

Bri giggles. "It's not what the map is," she teases, "it's what it can do."

Bri touches the little ship on the map labeled "*May Flower*" and whispers, "Shipwreck."

Suddenly, a door creaks open in the wall behind the map. I didn't remember seeing a door.

"Follow me!" Bri says, and we slip into the entrance. Without even a "whoosh," just like in my nightmare, I'm drifting down, down beneath dark waters.

I gasp in fear. Bri puts her hand on my shoulder and a sense of calm washes over me. I notice that although we seem to be deep in Lake Superior, I'm not getting wet, and I'm breathing normally.

"We're safe," Bri's voice reassures me. "This is all part of the magic of the map."

"No way! You've got to be kidding me!" I exclaim. "My dad is not going to believe this."

"Remember," she warns me. "It's a secret."

Before I can protest that I don't keep secrets from Dad, I'm standing next to a real shipwreck. On the side of the boat is a name: *May Flower*.

Bri continues as if this is the most ordinary thing for someone to do.

"This wreck was discovered in 1991, more than 100 years after it sank. Now it's on the National Register of Historic Places because so much can be learned about shipbuilding and maritime life in the late 1800s from it."

A shipwreck-hunting boat.

I stare at the water-soaked hull, the tumbled masts. Seeing a wreck on the floor of Lake Superior is as amazing as my dad describes it.

"Have you heard your dad talk about any shipwrecks?" Bri asks me as we stare at the remains of the *May Flower*.

"That's pretty much all he talks about," I say. "He was telling me about some of his favorite wrecks on Lake Superior on the ride here. He said there's a shipwreck with an interesting legend attached to it. It was called the *Western Reserve*."

"Let's learn more about that one," Bri says and directs me to say "*Western Reserve*."

Almost before I finish the name, we are transported. ⚓

Did you know?

You sometimes will see the name for the *May Flower* wrecked on Lake Superior spelled as one word like that original *Mayflower*. **Fun fact:** Boat names are written either in all capital letters LIKE THIS or in italics *like this*, probably so they aren't mistaken for the people for whom the boats are named.

A cleat on the *May Flower*. The boat was carrying sandstone for building a Duluth high school!

Anchor

Diver's tool bag

A diver's ditty bag for an archaeological survey might have clothes pins, a collapsible wooden measuring stick, a level, a slate, extra pencils, a hammer, nails and a plumb bob.

This is an anchor chain wound around the ship's windlass.

THE GRAPHIC
CHICAGO.
AN ILLUSTRATED
WEEKLY NEWSPAPER.
VOL. VII, NO. 12.   CHICAGO, SEPTEMBER 17, 1892.

Did you know?

Before photography became widely used, newspapers and magazines published woodcut drawings to illustrate stories, like this one showing the sinking of the *Western Reserve* used in The Graphic newspaper.

G.A COFFIN 92

LOSS OF THE "WESTERN RESERVE," OFF SABLE BANKS, LAKE SUPERIOR.

[DRAWN FOR THE GRAPHIC BY G. A. COFFIN, FROM A DESCRIPTION BY THE SOLE SURVIVOR.]

Western Reserve

We're back in the museum in front of a photo of the *Western Reserve*.

Did that really happen? Bri smiles, as if reading my mind, and tells me this is just the beginning of my adventures under the magic of the map.

Then, like my dad, Bri begins a little lecture. "Unlike the *May Flower* with its sails, the *Western Reserve* was a 300-foot-long propeller ship with an engine, one of the first bulk freighters made of steel plate and among the largest vessels at that time. With a steel hull, it could carry heavier loads than boats made of wood. In August 1892, the *Western Reserve* was heading from the lower Great Lakes across Lake Superior to Two Harbors, Minnesota, to load up with iron ore. Near Deer Park, Michigan, in the Upper Peninsula, it ran into a gale and broke in two on August 30. It sank in just 10 minutes. Out of 22 crewmen, only the wheelsman survived. He swam for two hours to a deserted shore, then walked 12 miles to a life-saving station. Do you want to check it out?"

"Heck, yah!"

"Well, let's head back to the map."

At the map, Bri tells me to transport us. I touch the drawing named *Western Reserve* and whisper, "Shipwreck." The door creaks open. I stare at Bri in disbelief, but she grabs my hand and plunges forward saying, "Here we go again!"

In the eerie glow at the bottom of the lake, we examine the remains of the *Western Reserve*. I suddenly remember that my dad said this wreck was never found ... and yet we seemed to have found it.

"Some say this ship was built with steel that was too brittle. Because of this accident, the U.S. Congress created new laws about testing the steel used in shipbuilding. Didn't you say your dad told you a legend about this boat?"

"Yes, he said that the owner of the ship was onboard with his family when it went down. Strangely, before it even happened, a local captain of the United States Life-saving Service dreamed about the accident. He dreamt in such detail that he recognized the body of Peter Minch, the owner, when he found Mr. Minch's body washed up on shore even though he'd never met him."

"I heard a story, too, about the *Western Reserve*," adds Bri. "I heard that the ship still makes ghostly appearances around Deer Park and on warm, calm nights, voices and laughter can be heard across the waves."

"No way!" I say in disbelief.

"Do you want to see another ship with a bizarre legend?" she asks.

"You bet I do!" This is really getting exciting.

"*Hudson*, shipwreck!" Bri calls out. ⚓

Hudson

"A horrible gale churned Lake Superior on September 15, 1901, as the 288-foot-long steel steamer, the *Hudson*, neared the Keweenaw Peninsula in Michigan. It was carrying a load of grain picked up in Duluth. The lighthouse keepers at Eagle River saw the twin-stacked ship dead in the water, leaning to one side before it suddenly rolled over and sank," Bri explains as we look at the wreck in the water before us. "It may have capsized because its cargo shifted to one side, which oily flax seeds are known to do, and the ship tipped over in the storm. A few days after the ship sank, a fishing boat found floating wreckage, including two masts that matched those of the *Hudson*. Over the next few days, more wreckage turned up. Sadly, so did the bodies of some crew, still wearing their life vests marked SS *Hudson*. But the ship was never seen again ... until it was found here in 2019 in 825 feet of water."

I ponder that ... 825 feet. I quickly calculate that at almost three football fields. That's way too deep to SCUBA dive, even for Dad. Yet how are we here under water?

I'm about to ask Bri when she catches my eye and says, "Are you ready for the ghost story?"

"Sure," I say, forgetting my question.

"There is a legend about this ship," Bri explains. "Supposedly, a tugboat captain and his mate were near Keweenaw Point on September 16 in the late 1940s. That's the same day 40 years earlier that the *Hudson* disappeared from view here. They saw a rusty ship, covered in brown slime, heading toward them. The tug captain barely missed crashing into it, then jumped onto the other ship to see if it was in distress. He was greeted by the ghosts of the *Hudson*'s captain and helmsman. They warned him to get off, and the tug captain wasted no time. He leapt off the *Hudson* into the icy lake water and swam back to his tug."

"Wow, that's creepy," I say. "What should we see next?"

"Let's do another sailing vessel," Bri suggests. We pop back into the museum, and I wonder how we're doing this. Reading my mind, Bri says, "After you first use the map magic, it's easier to come and go as you please. I've been doing this for a long, long time. ⚓

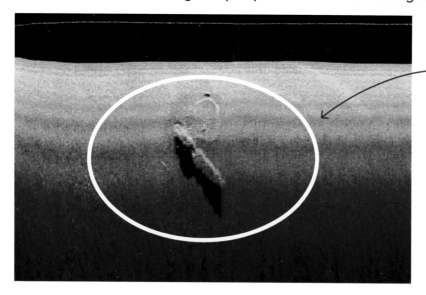

Shipwreck hunters use sonar-generated images, like this one, to locate underwater wrecks. Sonar uses sound waves to locate stuff.

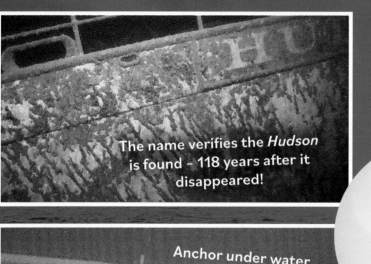

The name verifies the *Hudson* is found – 118 years after it disappeared!

Anchor under water.

Did you know?

At the time that it sank, the *Hudson* was one of the fastest ships on the Great Lakes. After the *Hudson* sank, wreckage from the ship was found on the water and along Michigan's shore for 25 miles, from Eagle River to Copper Harbor. Wreckage continued to toss up on the coast for days after the wreck.

Real Wreck Hunters
(Ken, Kraig, Jerry & Dan)

The *Hudson* at Houghton, Michigan ... on the water, not under it!

Part of the boat's oak framing.

What's in a Name?

Working boats on the Great Lakes often were named for people. It seems likely this boat was named for a mining and railroad businessman, Samuel Partridge Ely. It's said that Ely, Minnesota, was also named for him.

What's all that fur?

It's filamentous algae (like a seaweed).

The tow bit where *Ely*'s towline attached to the *Hesper*.

Samuel P. Ely

Standing in front of the map, Bri points to a wreck.

"Here's the *Samuel P. Ely*. It was a 200-foot wooden schooner with three tall masts. In October 1896, it was being towed by the steamship *Hesper* from Duluth to Two Harbors in Minnesota to pick up a load of iron ore when a big storm – the worst in 10 years – hit with winds gusting to 54 miles per hour and huge waves. For nine hours, the *Hesper* and the *Ely* battled the raging waves. As they neared Two Harbors, the gale winds were so bad that the *Hesper* cut the *Ely* loose or it broke free. The *Ely* blew across the harbor, crashed into a boat there and into the stone breakwall and wedged against the rocks. It couldn't be moved, and in the early morning, it sank. The crew escaped by clinging to the masts, which were still above the water. Fires were lit on Two Harbors' shore, and the tugboat *Ella G. Stone*, pulling a sailboat, headed out to rescue the crew. The tug let the sailboat drift near the sinking ship, and the men dropped into the sailboat to be pulled to shore. It took three trips, but all of them survived. Should we check it out?"

"Sure!" I reach out, touch the *Ely* and say, "Shipwreck."

"It looks like it's so close to the surface," I say as the *Samuel P. Ely* comes into sight.

"Right. It sits in only 29 feet of water just off the Two Harbors breakwall. As you can see, areas of the hull suffered damage, but the main part of the hull, which is the body of the ship, remains intact. Divers love to explore this shipwreck because it's not in very deep water."

When Bri mentioned deep water, I realize I've been so excited to see shipwrecks, I forgot about my fears.

"What's next?" I can't hide my excitement. ⚓

Where the mast fits.

A pump.

Thomas Wilson

"Hey, where are we?" I look around this weird-shaped building. It's not the visitor center, but we're not under water either.

Bri giggles. "We're by a whaleback freighter. This is the SS *Meteor*, and it's a museum in Superior, Wisconsin. Isn't it cool?"

"It sure is different from other museums I've been in. But why is it called a whaleback? There aren't any whales on the Great Lakes."

"No whales," agrees Bri, "but definitely whalebacks. These ships were designed for the Great Lakes right here in Superior by Captain Alexander McDougall. The SS *Meteor* is the last whaleback still above water."

"So why are we here?" I ask. "This boat isn't wrecked."

"I want you to see a whaleback above water, before we visit one below water called the *Thomas Wilson*. It was built here in Superior, too."

We walk inside to a picture of the *Thomas Wilson*, and I laugh out loud. "This looks like the cigar my grandpa smokes!"

"It does have a cigar shape, and when it's fully loaded, it looked like a whale in the water. It rode low, and with its curved hull, it went faster because it didn't have as much resistance from wind and waves."

"Can we see it?"

"Sure, it's not far from here ... just outside the Duluth-Superior Harbor at the Duluth entry."

We touch the picture and off we go! Hey, I think to myself, we didn't even need the magic map ... just Bri.

Standing under water in front of the *Thomas Wilson*, I say "Yep, just like my grandpa's cigar."

Bri begins, "This wreck shows that bad weather isn't the only reason boats sink. On June 7, 1902, it was filled with iron ore, heading out of the Duluth Ship Canal on a clear day with calm water. At the same time, the steamer *George G. Hadley* was entering the harbor. A tugboat captain told the *Hadley* to change course and head to Superior because all the coal docks at Duluth were full. In turning, *Hadley*'s captain didn't notice the *Wilson* and didn't blow the required whistle signals. The captain of the *Wilson* saw the *Hadley*. To avoid running aground on the port side (left), he turned to starboard (right). The *Hadley* struck the *Wilson*, rolling it. The *Wilson* righted itself, but began to sink. Within three minutes, it went under the water, drowning nine of the 20-man crew."

I am still staring at the odd shape of this wreck when Bri says, "This spot has seen other accidents. Do you want to hear about another?"

She really didn't even have to ask. ⚓

ew of the Harbor Conneaut, Ohio
Best regards from
ill write soon   Charles Mackey

You can visit the
SS *Meteor*!

Whalebacks have a
very special look

This is a "fairlead"
to help guide lines (the
ropes) from the boats.

Oops ...

Captain Alexander McDougall,
who designed the whalebacks,
is said to have claimed they
"can't be drowned. They'll ride
out any storm because the seas
will simply wash over them."
But storms aren't the only
thing that sinks ships ... sadly
for the *Thomas Wilson* and
its crew.

Divers are monitoring
changes at the *Wilson*
wreck site.

Mataafa

Back inside the maritime visitor center, Bri starts telling me about a deadly storm in 1905.

"It was November 27. Twenty-nine ships were wrecked, damaged or disappeared on Lake Superior that day and the next day, and 36 people died on the Big Lake."

I ask her what happened.

"Well, it was two days before Thanksgiving," she starts, "when one of the worst storms in Lake Superior history began."

Bri stops in front of a photo.

"This is the *Mataafa*. The 4,840-ton steamship was towing a 3,422-ton barge *James Nasmyth* when it reached the piers of the Duluth Ship Canal during the winter storm. Afraid the *Mataafa* couldn't safely tow the barge into the harbor, the captain unhooked it from the barge and shot the *Mataafa*, full-steam, toward the canal and its safe harbor. Instead, a giant wave tossed the *Mataafa* down on the north pier, puncturing the hull. The *Mataafa* drifted backward and got hung up on a sandbar not far from the shore, but too far for its crew to risk swimming in this storm. The life-saving station rescuers used rowboats back then, and they couldn't help. Sadly, with perhaps 10,000 people on shore that night lighting fires to support them, nine of the 24 crewmen died, many freezing to death in the stern, or the back, of the ship because they couldn't get to the front, or bow, of the boat. In those days, there was no way to walk inside the ship from back to front when it was loaded. I remember my heart sank for all those people. The storm is remembered as the *Mataafa* Storm or *Mataafa* Blow of 1905."

Bri continues, "We can't go visit the wreck because the boat was repaired and served another 60 years before being scrapped."

I want to learn more about that storm, so I ask if there are any other shipwrecks from that day that we can see under the water.

"There are many," says Bri, "but I like the one that helped to create a lighthouse."

She reaches out her hand, I touch it and ... ⚓

So close but too far ... the *Mataafa* was almost to shore.

In 1905, rescuers had to row.

Weird but true

After the tragedy on the *Mataafa*, the accident was remembered on a colorful cigar box. Black-and-white picture postcards were sold showing the ship as it lay stuck near the shore of Duluth.

MATAAFA

TITLE AND DESIGN REGISTERED BY DULUTH CIGAR CO.

STEAMER "MATAAFA" WRECKED OFF PIER OF DULUTH SHIP CANAL, DURING THE GREAT STORM OF NOV. 28, 1905. NINE MEN WERE LOST FROM THIS VESSEL.

THE CALVERT LITH. CO. DETROIT & CHICAGO

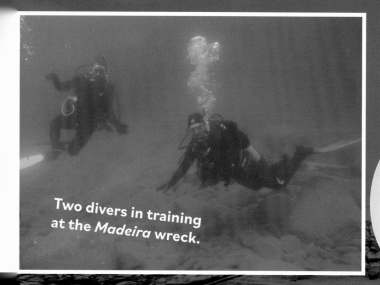

Two divers in training at the *Madeira* wreck.

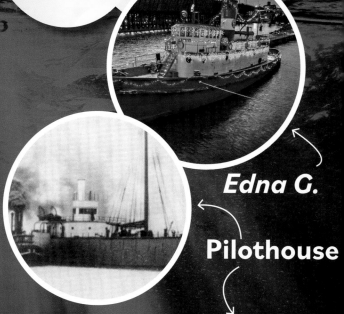

Edna G.

Pilothouse

A diver swims by a deck winch on the *Madeira*. Is the boat tilted or the photo? The diver's air bubbles give a clue.

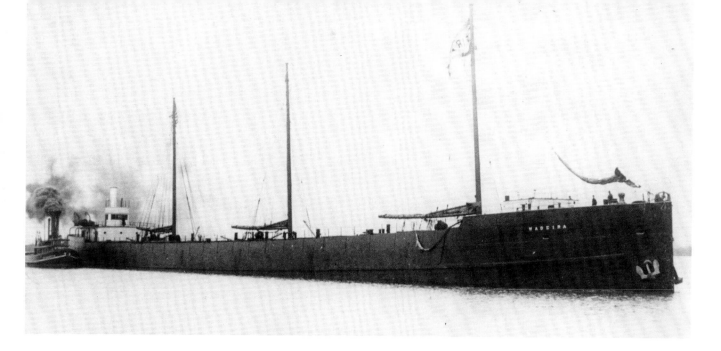

Madeira

We're standing outside a lighthouse I recognize from many photos I've seen: the golden tower of Split Rock Lighthouse high on a rocky cliff on Minnesota's North Shore.

Unlike our visits under water, where I never got wet, I can feel the wind tear at my shirt. I wish I had my jacket. Bri seems not to notice, except to say, "The wind blew hard that day, too, in 1905 when the *Madeira*, a steel barge, was being towed by the *William Edenborn*.

"As the story goes, winds were 70 to 80 miles an hour, blowing snow onto the deck and kicking up huge waves. Fearing he'd lose his ship, the captain of the *Edenborn* cut the towline, just like the *Mataafa* unhooked from its barge. And just like the *Mataafa*, cutting its tow barge free didn't help the *Edenborn*. It washed aground and broke in two. Meanwhile, the *Madeira* crashed into Gold Rock cliff. As the hull pounded broadside against the rocky cliff, the ship began to break up. Do you want to go check it out?"

We walk from the lighthouse over to where an info sign describes the *Madeira* wreck.

"We are looking at Gold Rock," Bri points across the water at another cliff. "The *Madeira* crashed there. Some of it lies only 20 feet below the water, but other parts of the ship rest 110 feet deep. It's a popular shipwreck dive because some of it's so close to the surface, and despite being more than a century in the water, it still looks like a ship.

"There are many amazing things about the *Madeira* and its destruction. It's one of the few known examples of a steel-hulled schooner barge that still exists, even though it's under Lake Superior. This wreck, and others damaged along Minnesota's North Shore during the 1905 storm, caused the U.S. Congress to build Split Rock Lighthouse in 1910. Many ships and lives were saved because of the lighthouse."

"That is amazing," I agree.

"But best of all," continues Bri, "is how the *Madeira* crew was saved."

"How?"

Bri smiles with a far-off look, as if remembering the day herself. "The story goes that the 10 crew members would most likely have died, if not for a hero, Fred Benson. Fred grabbed

Everything used to build the lighthouse was hauled from the water up the 130-foot cliff because there were no roads on the North Shore back then. Gold Rock cliff, where *Madeira* sank, is 60 feet.

a line and jumped from the deck of the ship onto a rock sticking out at the base of the steep cliff. Then, with storm waves crashing against him, he scrambled 60 feet to the top of Gold Rock cliff. From there, he dropped the line, weighted down with a rock, to the deck at the bow of the boat. Three men trapped there climbed to land. Then Fred dropped the line onto the stern deck, and five more men climbed to safety. The first mate, who had tried to climb the mast to reach the cliff that way, was tossed off and drowned, but he was the only crew member lost. Two days later, the tugboat *Edna G.* rescued the stranded crewmen from the cliff.

"What a hero!" I exclaim.

As if reading my mind, Bri says, "The *Edna G.* was a hero, too. Let's go back to the visitor center, and I'll show you a picture of this hard-working tug."

Standing in front of a picture of the *Edna G.*, Bri has more information for me. "The *Edna G.* is a tugboat with a 1,000-horsepower engine. A typical race car has about 800-horsepower. In its day, it burned 25 tons of coal a week to build-up steam while moving ships and barges carrying iron ore and taconite out of Two Harbors. In 1974, it was named a National Historic Site, since it was the only steam-powered tug operating on the Great Lakes. You can still see it in Two Harbors because it was donated to the city after it retired."

Once again Bri surprises me, and I ask, "How do you know all of this?"

"Like I said ... it's kind of my thing," she says with a wink and a smile. ⚓

Amboy

Back in the maritime visitor center, we walk along the hallway where the old photos line the walls, and the name of one catches my eye.

"Hey, I remember this one," I tell Bri excitedly.

"The *Amboy*," says Bri. "Yes, it also sank in the *Mataafa* Storm in 1905. The *Amboy* was a single-decked, wooden-hulled, three-masted schooner constructed specially to carry iron ore. The steamer *George Spencer* was towing it to Duluth when both ships wrecked where Taconite Harbor is today. Did you know iron ore is used to make steel?"

I pick up the story, happy to finally have my own information to share. "My dad told me the *Amboy* ran up on the rocks, and for 13 hours, the crew battled the crashing waves and chilling snow. As soon as the boat struck the rocks, the crew threw buoys with lines over the side. When the buoys floated ashore, fisherman caught them to use as life lines. Fishermen even rushed into the water up to their necks to help crew members escape. Everyone got to shore safely," I say, proud to teach Bri something for a change, though from her smile I think she already knew.

"Remains of both ships still lie on the shore," I say.

"So anyone can go there to see an actual shipwreck without getting wet," Bri adds. ⚓

Unlike some ships sunk in the *Mataafa* Storm, the *Amboy* beached on sand and broke apart.

An on-land wreck

Part of the *Amboy* wreck is on land. (You can see it in the photo on the facing page). Some is under water so the wreck is in "2 to 15 feet" of water. The hull planking and frames in this picture are from the *George Spencer*, which sank next to the *Amboy*.

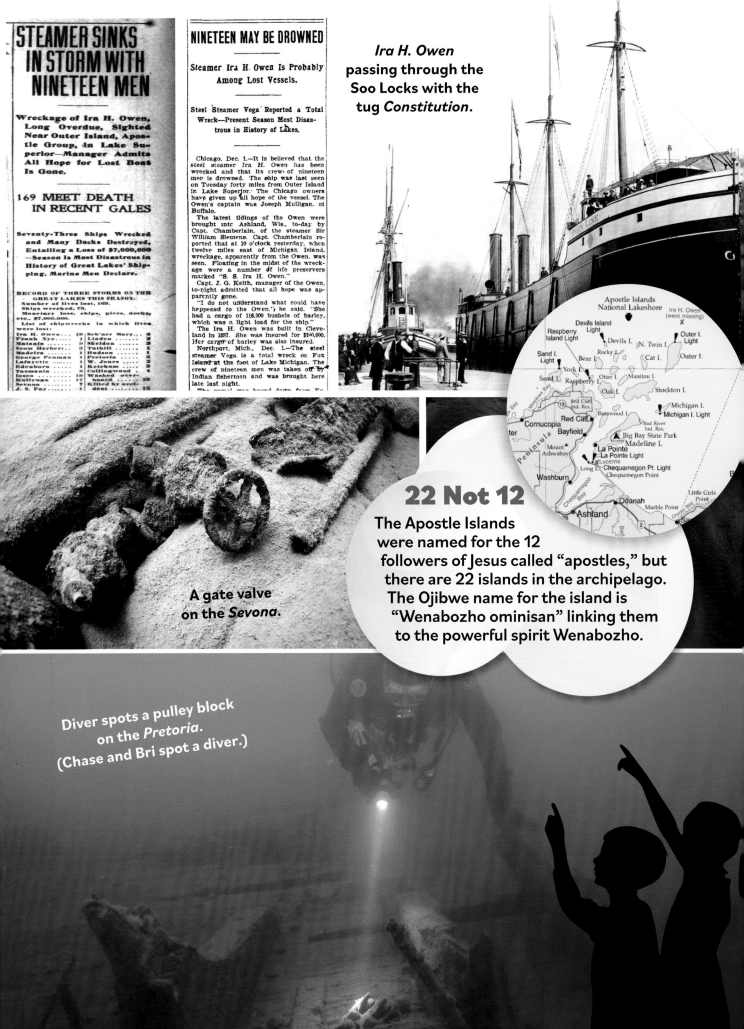

STEAMER SINKS IN STORM WITH NINETEEN MEN

Wreckage of Ira H. Owen, Long Overdue, Sighted Near Outer Island, Apostle Group, in Lake Superior—Manager Admits All Hope for Lost Boat Is Gone.

169 MEET DEATH IN RECENT GALES

Seventy-Three Ships Wrecked and Many Docks Destroyed, Entailing a Loss of $7,000,000 —Season Is Most Disastrous in History of Great Lakes' Shipping, Marine Men Declare.

RECORD OF THREE STORMS ON THE GREAT LAKES THIS SEASON.
Number of lives lost, 169.
Ships wrecked, 73.
Monetary loss, ships, piers, docks, etc., $7,000,000.
List of shipwrecks in which lives were lost:

Ira H. Owen...	19	Sch'ner Mary...	6
Frank Nye.....	1	Linden	1
Matanfa	1	Sheldon	2
Scow Herbert..	3	Tuthill	1
Madeira	1	Hudson	1
George Penman	3	Pretoria	5
Lafayette	1	W. Jones	2
Edenborn	1	Ketchum	3
Tasmania	1	Collingwood ..	1
Iosco	19	Washed over-	
Kaliyuga	17	board	1
Sevona	7	Killed by acci-	
J. S. Fay.....	1	dent	15

NINETEEN MAY BE DROWNED

Steamer Ira H. Owen Is Probably Among Lost Vessels.

Steel Steamer Vega Reported a Total Wreck—Present Season Most Disastrous in History of Lakes.

Chicago, Dec. 1.—It is believed that the steel steamer Ira H. Owen has been wrecked and that its crew of nineteen men is drowned. The ship was last seen on Tuesday forty miles from Outer Island in Lake Superior. The Chicago owners have given up all hope of the vessel. The Owen's captain was Joseph Mulligan, of Buffalo.

The latest tidings of the Owen were brought into Ashland, Wis., to-day by Capt. Chamberlain, of the steamer Sir William Siemens. Capt. Chamberlain reported that at 10 o'clock yesterday, when twelve miles east of Michigan Island, wreckage, apparently from the Owen, was seen. Floating in the midst of the wreckage were a number of life preservers marked "S. S. Ira H. Owen."

Capt. J. G. Keith, manager of the Owen, to-night admitted that all hope was apparently gone.

"I do not understand what could have happened to the Owen." he said. "She had a cargo of 116,000 bushels of barley, which was a light load for the ship."

The Ira H. Owen was built in Cleveland in 1887. She was insured for $100,000. Her cargo of barley was also insured.

Northport, Mich., Dec. 1.—The steel steamer Vega is a total wreck on Fox Island at the foot of Lake Michigan. The crew of nineteen men was taken off by Indian fishermen and was brought here late last night.

Ira H. Owen passing through the Soo Locks with the tug *Constitution*.

A gate valve on the *Sevona*.

22 Not 12

The Apostle Islands were named for the 12 followers of Jesus called "apostles," but there are 22 islands in the archipelago. The Ojibwe name for the island is "Wenabozho ominisan" linking them to the powerful spirit Wenabozho.

Diver spots a pulley block on the *Pretoria*. (Chase and Bri spot a diver.)

Wrecks of the Apostles

"Did you know," Bri says, "that one ship disappeared completely during the *Mataafa* Storm in 1905?"

"Was it by Split Rock Lighthouse?"

"No, it happened by the Apostle Islands."

I'm not sure where the Apostle Islands are, so Bri takes me back to the shipwreck map and points off the northern coast of Wisconsin.

"This is the Apostle Islands National Lakeshore that runs 12 miles along the shore and includes 21 islands. There are 22 islands in the Apostle's archipelago, but Madeline Island has year-round residents and is not part of the national park," she says. "The *Ira H. Owen* was last seen here, off Outer Island, heading down the lake carrying a load of 116,000 bushels of barley."

I know the map magic can conjure up the ship, even if it's missing, but we settle for a photograph of the *Ira H. Owen* instead.

Standing in front of the photo, Bri shakes her head. "This poor freighter had so many accidents it seemed doomed from the start. Launched in July 1887, it was one of the first steel-hulled freighters on the Great Lakes. In November that year, the *Owen* ran aground near the Soo Locks. In June 1892, it collided with the schooner *Belle Brown* in a heavy fog. In July 1897, it collided with the steamer *Susquehanna*, also in heavy fog. In 1903, a fire started in the *Owen*'s boiler room. In October 1904, it collided with another steel steamer, *Henry W. Oliver*."

I can't help but think that was one unlucky boat.

"Each time, it was repaired. But on the morning of November 28, 1905, the *Ira H. Owen* left Duluth on its last voyage. The weather was getting worse as it passed the Apostle Islands. As it steamed by Outer Island, a furious wind picked up, whipping snow onto the deck as waves pounded it and its 19 crew members.

"The captain of a nearby ship, the *Harold B. Nye*, heard the constant blowing of distress signals, but the *Nye* was in so much trouble itself, it couldn't help. Dense snow blocked the view of the *Ira H. Owen* and when the crew of the *Nye* could finally see, the *Owen* was gone. Vanished."

"Gone, without a trace!" I stammer. "That poor crew."

"It reminds me of a dark day earlier that year in the Apostle Islands," Bri adds thoughtfully. "Two ships wrecked in a horrible blow on September 2, 1905. The steamer *Sevona*, loaded with about 6,000 tons of iron ore, left the Allouez docks in Superior the night before. By the time it reached outside of the islands, the wind howled and the waves roared. The captain tried to find shelter, but the *Sevona* struck a shoal northeast of Sand Island, causing one mighty crash, then two more loud crashes. The ship broke in the middle and gradually sank, stuck on the rocks of the shoal. At daylight came another splintering noise, and the stuck ship snapped in two. Four women and seven crewmen got into a lifeboat in the water. One woman later described their fight to keep the small lifeboat upright in the storm for five hours. She said if not for an engineer onboard with expert rowing skills, they would have died. Finally a large lifesaving wave lifted the lifeboat and carried it safely onto the sand beach. Another lifeboat with six crewmen behind them disappeared from sight, and it was feared they drowned. Luckily instead, the wind and waves drove them onto Sand Island. Seven other crew members, stuck on the forward half of the divided *Sevona*, struggled against the huge waves going clear over the top of it, but they drowned in sight of shore."

Before I catch my breath, Bri continues with one more.

"Leaving the same Superior dock that night as the *Sevona* was the *Pretoria*, 338-foot wooden schooner barge. It was under tow by the steamer *Venezuela* with a load of iron ore. As the *Pretoria* neared the Apostle Islands, the steering gear failed. The towline connecting the two boats tore apart, and the *Pretoria* drifted toward the islands, slowly beaten up by crashing waves. The *Pretoria*'s anchor was dropped, and it finally caught and held within 1-1/2 miles off of Outer Island. The battered ship continued to break apart. The captain and nine crewmen abandoned ship, but their lifeboat overturned in the powerful waves and five of them drowned. The survivors were taken to the Outer Island lighthouse. The *Pretoria* sank in 54 feet of water, with only its tall masts still sticking above the surface."

My sadness at the loss of people and ships must show on my face. Bri touches my shoulder lightly and asks, "Would you like to visit a different place ... and learn about Lake Superior's most famous ghost ship?"

Before I finish my nod, the Lake Superior Maritime Visitor Center fades from my view, and I am standing outside a new lighthouse, this one blazing red. ⚓

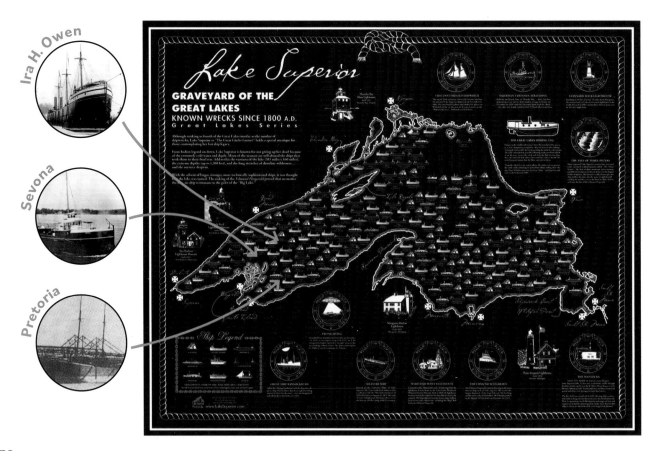

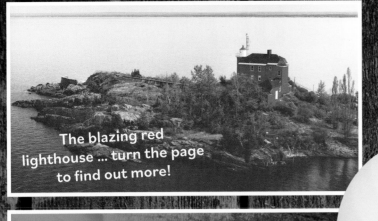

The blazing red lighthouse ... turn the page to find out more!

turn the page to find out more!

Did you know?

Underwater archaeologist is a real job ... like for Tamara Thomsen pictured here! Such experts in history and in diving record shipwrecks and other underwater historical sites. Diving in Lake Superior can get very cold. The lake temperature averages about 40° F ... about the same as inside your refrigerator!

A hawsepipe (the name of the pipe for the anchor chain) on the *Pretoria*.

She took these!

See the V?

These pipes ran through the *Sevona*.

Sevona's shark fins??! No, it's the mount for the ship's boiler (used to generate steam).

An access port on the *Sevona*.

Bannockburn

"Welcome to the retired red lighthouse for Marquette, Michigan's U.S. Coast Guard station," says Bri casually. "It's part of the Marquette Maritime Museum."

"Wait, we're in Michigan?" I ask, astounded.

"Yes, on the north side of the Upper Peninsula. Come inside," she continues without pause, "and I'll tell you another ghost ship story."

Inside, we find a photo of a ship called the *Bannockburn*.

"This steel-hulled freighter from Canada is the *Flying Dutchman* of Lake Superior."

"*Flying Dutchman*?" I ask. "What's that?"

"The *Flying Dutchman* disappeared on the ocean and was doomed to sail forever. Legend says it returns time and again to warn of pending trouble for other ships," Bri explains.

"So why is *Bannockburn* called that?"

Bri chuckles and shakes her head. "Let me tell the story first ...

"On November 21, 1902, *Bannockburn* left Port Arthur, which today is part of Thunder Bay, Ontario, on its way to the Soo Locks. It had to travel all the way across Lake Superior, west to east, about 350 miles. The nine-year-old, 1,620-ton steel-hulled steamer was carrying 85,000 bushels of wheat. Trouble started early. The freighter ran aground on its way out of Port Arthur, but got off without damage. As the *Bannockburn* headed east that night, a strong winter storm blew in and lasted several days. During the night, the crew of the *Huronic*, a passenger steamer, spotted the *Bannockburn*. The *Huronic*'s own engines were damaged in that storm, but it arrived safely in port. The *Bannockburn* was not so lucky. It, and the 21 people on it, were never seen again ... or at least not alive."

"Really, nothing was ever found?" I ask.

"Well, a battered life jacket and an oar with the name *Bannockburn* scraped into the wood and wrapped in tarp were found. To this day the disappearance of the *Bannockburn* remains a mystery."

"Hey," I suddenly remember Bri's words. "What did you mean the ship and crew weren't seen 'alive' again?"

"This is why the *Bannockburn* is called the *Flying Dutchman* of Lake Superior. Some sailors claim that on icy or stormy nights, the ghostly presence of the *Bannockburn* pierces through the gloom, sailing fast to nowhere. So many ships have disappeared on Lake Superior," Bri shakes her head, then adds, "Let me tell you about the lost minesweepers." ⚓

Ghost Ships!

There is a long maritime tradition of ghost ships – ships that have gone missing – being spotted by sailors during or just before times of great peril. One theory of what happened to the *Bannockburn* is that it hit the peak of an underwater mountain on Lake Superior called the Superior Shoal. That may also be the cause of the lost minesweepers ... read on!

NAVARIN

Building a minesweeper at Canadian Car in Fort William.

SEBASTOPOL, INKERMANN, CERISOLES

Isle Royale

Keweenaw Peninsula

INKERMANN & CERISOLES

?

Manitou Island

Bete Gris

SEBASTO

SEBASTO

Minesweepers waiting to sail through the Great Lakes & across the Atlantic Ocean to France.

Check out the big gun!

Finished boats were brought to the nearby water on tracks.

This one has the French flag!

Jul 29-18

The Lost Minesweepers

"The lost what?" I'm totally confused.

"Minesweepers," repeats Bri. "They are small warships sent out to remove or set off naval mines."

"You mean like bombs under water?" Now I am interested.

"Exactly. They have 'sweeps' on board that are mechanical or electrical devices that cut the cables that anchor the mines in place or disable the mines."

"Wow! How come these are 'lost' minesweepers?"

Bri waits a moment. "It happened in World War I in 1918. The French government bought a dozen minesweepers that were built in the old city of Fort William, Ontario. All but the last three had sailed across Lake Superior and out to the ocean. Those three had to sail across the lake in late fall, a dangerous time. On November 23, 1918, the *Inkerman*, *Cerisoles* and *Sebastopol* left Fort William heading toward the Soo Locks. Each ship had a full French Navy crew plus a Canadian ship pilot (an experienced Great Lakes captain) to navigate them. As they moved across the open lake, a blizzard sprang up with 50 mile per hour winds and 30-foot waves. All three ships lost sight of each other through the snow, wind and waves. The storm pounded *Sebastopol* for two days, and the crew feared they would not survive. According to reports, a sailor said, 'The storm was so bad we had to get out the lifeboats and put on lifebelts. The boat almost sank, and it was nearly goodbye to anyone hearing from us again. You can believe me, I will always remember that day.' *Sebastopol* did reach the locks at Sault Ste. Marie. It left downbound to the lower Great Lakes, confident the other minesweepers would follow, but the two ships and their crews were never seen."

"What do you think happened to them?"

Bri hesitates, as if deciding what to tell me. Finally, she says simply, "Nobody knows."

"But wouldn't someone have found them eventually?"

"Not yet ... that's why it's a mystery." Bri winks. "What caused the next shipwreck is no mystery at all. Ready for another?" ⚓

Did you know?

Michigan Technological University did the map (facing page) showing where the two minesweepers likely traveled and disappeared. The Great Lakes Shipwreck Historical Society, using the research vessel *David Boyd* (shown here) is searching for those ships. Perhaps they won't be lost for much longer!

Gunilda

We walk to a photograph of a great looking yacht that I bet was super fast.

"The *Gunilda* went down along Lake Superior's northern shore up in Ontario," starts Bri. "It was a beautiful boat, the pride of its owner, William Harkness. He was one of the richest men in the world and owned part of the Standard Oil Company."

"That is a beautiful yacht," I agree.

"You mean it *was* a beautiful yacht," teases Bri. "Mr. Harkness was known for cutting corners when it came to spending money. He took his family and some friends on a cruise during the summer of 1911. He knew the channel would be tricky as they got near Ontario, so he asked about hiring a local captain to pilot the boat. Mr. Harkness thought the price was too high, so he had his own captain continue navigating, even though his own captain advised against that. Let's get back to the shipwreck map so you can see it firsthand."

"Wait a minute," I say. "The shipwreck map is here in Marquette, too?"

"Of course," says Bri, and sure enough, the map is on the wall next to her. She points to a spot along the northern shore. "*Gunilda*, shipwreck."

Once again below the water, Bri continues, "The morning of August 29, 1911, was foggy, and the *Gunilda* ended up slamming into McGarvey Shoal near Rossport. Mr. Harkness arranged for a tugboat, the *James Whalen*, to pull the *Gunilda* off the rocks. The tug captain arrived with a barge and recommended getting a second barge to form a sling to keep the

yacht firmly held between them. Mr. Harkness refused to pay for the second barge, and when the *Gunilda* was tugged free, it rolled onto its side and the masts hit the lake. As the yacht began to fill with water and sink, all the people scrambled to safety aboard the tugboat. The yacht sank 280 feet to the bottom."

"I guess that's what happens when pride gets in the way. It lost him his yacht and almost his family and friends," I say. Looking at the sunken yacht under the water, I think it still looks beautiful and eerie.

"I agree. I have one more 'gone missing' wreck to show you - one that was discovered 100 years after it sank." ⚓

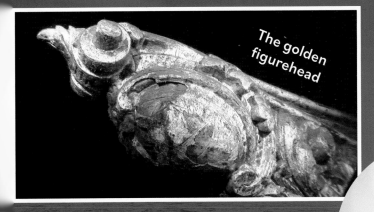
The golden figurehead

Which part of the ship is this?

Telegraph for engine orders

Here's something you don't see every day on a boat ... a lounge with a fireplace! There was also a piano in the game room.

Diver meets figurehead!

Heroic Storm

After the 1913 storm, U.S. Life-saving crews at Eagle Harbor and Portage, Michigan, were awarded Gold Lifesaving Medals of Honor. The two crews braved hurricane winds, blizzard snows and freezing waves to save a ship. The *Henry B. Smith* was not so lucky. It would take 100 years to find it at the location marked here with an X.

Posing for a ship "selfie" before cell phones.

Henry B. Smith

"The ship I want to show you is the *Henry B. Smith*," says Bri back inside Marquette's red lighthouse. "It sank just about 30 miles north of here."

Bri takes me to a picture of the *Henry B. Smith*. "This ship was massive. It was a steel-hulled freighter, carrying 9,500 tons of iron ore. It went down during the Storm of 1913, one of the biggest storms ever recorded on the Great Lakes. The storm is sometimes called the White Hurricane because the winds reached hurricane-speeds of 90 miles per hour plus it was also a snowstorm. The storm sank 12 ships and battered 31 more against the rocks or shore from Lake Superior to Lake Erie. One of those lost was the *Henry B. Smith*. It was sailing from Marquette, Michigan, to Cleveland, Ohio, carrying iron ore. All 25 people on the ship died."

Bri stops for a moment to honor to all those who died, then we transport to the wreck.

"What's strange about the *Henry B. Smith* is it went missing in November 1913 and remained undiscovered until May 2013, when a group of shipwreck hunters found it. Yes, almost 100 years exactly after it went missing."

My eyes get big as I look at this huge freighter. We walk (but weirdly are not swimming) to the front of the boat. I can't help thinking how exciting it must have been for those wreck hunters to discover it. Maybe my dad knows them.

"Speaking of those wreck hunters, they also found other shipwrecks around the Apostles – the *Moonlight* in 2004, the *Marquette* in 2005 and the *Antelope* in 2016. They are all wooden ships."

"How exciting! You know, I may try diving. I've got a pretty good teacher right at home!" I smile.

"OK, *Henry B. Smith* … see ya later," says Bri. "Next up, the museum at the heart of the Shipwreck Coast and from there to wrecks near a special island." ⚓

Kamloops

Suddenly we are on a long sandy beach looking out at Lake Superior. I see a freighter in the distance. Behind us rises an unusual looking lighthouse tower made all of steel and painted white with a red top. Many white buildings surround it.

"This is the Great Lakes Shipwreck Museum at the farthest northeastern tip of Michigan's Upper Peninsula," explains Bri.

This time, I'm not even really surprised we traveled so far in just a minute.

"This is right along the Shipwreck Coast," she adds.

"What's the Shipwreck Coast?"

"It's a 52-mile stretch along the shore between Marquette and Whitefish Point where more than 300 ships ran aground and went to their watery graves. So many shipwrecks," Bri says, shaking her head.

"Would you like to see one that's popular with the best divers?"

"Yeah," I say, thinking that maybe I'll have something in common with Dad after all. I know he's one of the best divers on the Great Lakes.

We walk inside one of the museum buildings and sure enough, there is the dark map.

Pointing to what some call the wolf's eye of Lake Superior, Bri says, "This is Isle Royale. It's the largest island in Lake Superior. This island

An underwater clue!

Did you know?

The *Kamloops* is the deepest of the wrecks identified within Isle Royale National Park. Because deep dives can be dangerous, wreck hunters may use an ROV - a remotely operated vehicle - to explore a ship. It is often attached to a host ship and may be equipped with a video camera, lights and a sonar system.

Lights!

A shoe?

An ROV visiting the *Kamloops* propeller.

Kamloops ship's wheel!

Cumberland side wheel!

10 to Note

There are 10 major shipwrecks identified within the boundaries of Isle Royale National Park:

- *Algoma*, a passenger steamer that broke in half in 1885;
- *America*, a steel passenger steamer that sank in 1928;
- *Henry Chisholm*, a bulk freighter that sank in 1898;
- *Chester A. Congdon*, also a bulk freighter, sank in 1918;
- *George M. Cox*, a passenger steamer that sank in 1933;
- *Cumberland*, a side-wheel passenger steamer that sank in 1877;
- *Emperor*, a bulk freighter that sank in 1947;
- *Glenlyon*, another bulk freighter that sank in 1924;
- *Monarch*, a package freighter that sank in 1906.
- *Kamloops*, a package freighter that sank in 1927.

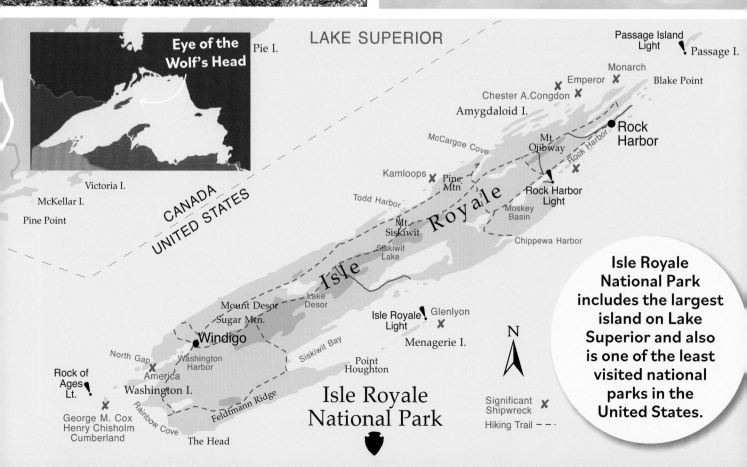

Eye of the Wolf's Head

LAKE SUPERIOR

Pie I.

Passage Island Light — Passage I.

Monarch

Emperor — Blake Point

Chester A. Congdon

Amygdaloid I.

McCargoe Cove

Mt. Ojibway

Rock Harbor

Kamloops — Pine Mtn

Rock Harbor Light

Todd Harbor

Isle Royale

Moskey Basin

Victoria I.

CANADA

UNITED STATES

McKellar I.

Pine Point

Mt. Siskiwit

Siskiwit Lake

Chippewa Harbor

Mount Desor

Lake Desor

Sugar Mtn.

Windigo

Isle Royale Light — Glenlyon

Menagerie I.

North Gap

Washington Harbor

Siskiwit Bay

Point Houghton

N

Rock of Ages Lt.

America

Washington I.

George M. Cox
Henry Chisholm
Cumberland

Rainbow Cove

Feldtmann Ridge

The Head

Isle Royale National Park

Significant Shipwreck ✕

Hiking Trail - - -

Isle Royale National Park includes the largest island on Lake Superior and also is one of the least visited national parks in the United States.

and those around it make up Isle Royale National Park. More than 25 ships have been wrecked around these islands, and the park has its own team of diving rangers. Most wrecks happened when the ships struck a reef during storms. But one was different. I want you to see it!"

She touches a ship with the name *Kamloops*, and we are deep in the water again.

"The *Kamloops* was a 250-foot steel package freighter, which meant it could carry just about anything but oil. It disappeared in December 1927 with 22 people onboard. It was last seen steaming towards Isle Royale, heavily coated in ice. It vanished without a trace for the next 50 years. This ship was finally found in August 1977, very close to the northwest shore of Isle Royale, by a group of sport divers. The cause of the ship's sinking is still a mystery because, as you can see, its hull is mostly undamaged but it's lying on its side." Bri smiles slyly and looks around her before whispering, "The *Kamloops* is said to have a ghost."

"Tell me!" I urged. I know Dad visited this wreck, but I don't remember a ghost story.

"Well," begins Bri, "some divers reported seeing the pale white ghost relaxing in one of the crew bunks, quietly watching the divers make their way through the ship. Other divers say the ghost they call 'Grandpa' would wander inside the boat, going about his business as if he were still alive and apparently unaware the ship was sitting in 260 feet of water on the bottom of Lake Superior."

"That's freaky," I say, feeling a wee bit uncomfortable and looking behind me.

Bri chuckles, and in an instant, we are standing half in, half out of the water. Below us, almost at the surface it seems, is another wreck. ⚓

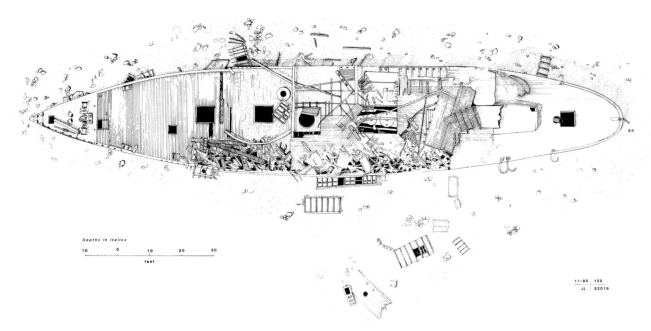

Depths in Italics
10   0   10   20   30
feet

11-86 | 139
JL | 82018

America

"We're almost completely on the west end of Isle Royale," says Bri, then adds as she points down. "And this is what remains of an excursion boat named *America*."

"What did it carry?" I ask.

"It transported passengers, mail and packages. The *America* sailed a regular route along Minnesota's North Shore from Duluth to Isle Royale on to the old cities of Port Arthur and Fort William in Ontario."

We sink lower, facing the bow of the *America*, which angles deeper into the water.

Bri continues the story. "People living seasonally on Isle Royale would wait for it to arrive to bring or pick up the mail and guests to the resorts. It also picked up wooden kegs and crates of fish from the commercial fishermen living on the island. Because the shipwreck is so close to the surface, some people say the *America* welcomes visitors to Isle Royale as they pass through Washington Harbor.

"The remains of the *America* are only a few feet below the surface. It sits along a steep underwater cliff, in some places as deep as 85 feet and as shallow as 2 feet from the surface. In June 1928, it left the Windigo resort dock at the head of the harbor and hit an underwater shoal. The shoal tore a hole in the hull. The captain yelled, 'Beach her! Beach her!' hoping to settle on sand, but the *America* struck hard on another shoal and sank. All passengers and crew made it safely to lifeboats, except, sadly, one dog was tied to the aft railing and could not be saved. The ship started to deteriorate quickly because of waves near the surface hitting it. The cool thing is, in 1996 the Great Lakes Shipwreck Preservation Society took on the job of restoring it. An underwater preservation of a shipwreck had never been attempted before that time."

"I bet lots of divers get to explore the *America* since it's in such shallow water," I say. Then I repeat a question I had asked at the beginning of the day. "Bri, is there a shipwreck that's special to you?" ⚓

The *America* sits at an angle, part of it almost at the surface and part of it 85 feet under water.

Going up?

Deep Diving

Diving more than 50 feet under water requires special skills and equipment. Divers with the National Park Service, both from Isle Royale and the Submerged Resources Center have been documenting the wrecks around the island and using 360° cameras so one day you can see the wrecks as if you are really there via a special head set.

Another staircase from the *America* is on display in the Great Lakes Aquarium in Duluth.

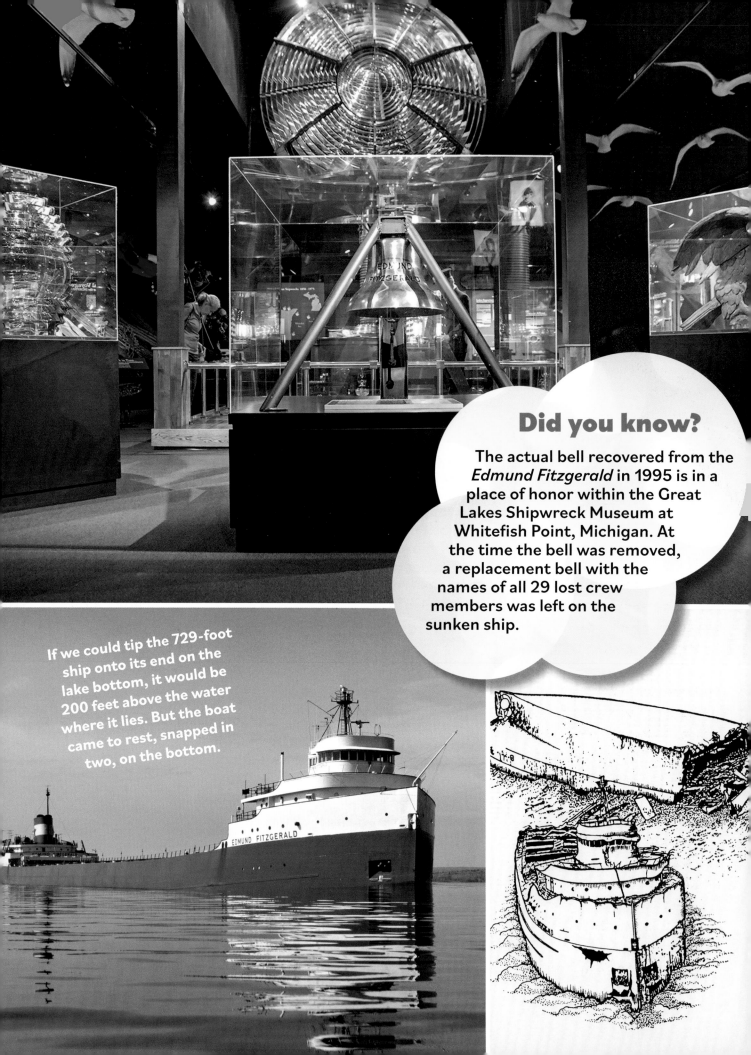

Did you know?

The actual bell recovered from the *Edmund Fitzgerald* in 1995 is in a place of honor within the Great Lakes Shipwreck Museum at Whitefish Point, Michigan. At the time the bell was removed, a replacement bell with the names of all 29 lost crew members was left on the sunken ship.

If we could tip the 729-foot ship onto its end on the lake bottom, it would be 200 feet above the water where it lies. But the boat came to rest, snapped in two, on the bottom.

Edmund Fitzgerald

"For that one," Bri says, "we need to return to Whitefish Point."

Almost as she says it, we are again in the Great Lakes Shipwreck Museum. Bri walks to a display with a bell illuminated by a glowing light. "This museum has the actual bell recovered from the wreck of the *Edmund Fitzgerald*."

I seem to remember that name from Dad's lectures.

Bri continues. "The *Fitz*, as it was nicknamed, was a 729-foot lake freighter, the largest one sailing at the time. It carried iron ore. It started its final voyage from Superior, Wisconsin. It is one of the most famous shipwrecks of Lake Superior because it was the largest ship to sink on the Great Lakes and is one of the most recent shipwrecks. It sank shortly after 7:10 p.m. on November 10, 1975, about 17 miles from Whitefish Bay. After hours of struggling in the violent waves of the winter storm, the last words heard on the radio from the ship's captain were, 'We are holding our own.' If only that had been true. Sadly, it's in 535 feet of water on the Canadian side of the lake. One reason it remains important is that all 29 crew members died. There are still memorial services today every November 10, here at Whitefish Point, at Split Rock Lighthouse and in Detroit."

"That's a lot of lost lives," I say sadly. "What exactly happened?"

"It was truly tragic," she says, walking us toward a painting of the *Fitz* with giant waves crashing against it. It takes my breath away as memories of my nightmare flash back to me.

Bri doesn't seem to notice. "The boat was caught in a severe storm with near hurricane-force winds and waves 35 feet tall."

"That would be like almost seven of my dad all stacked up!" I try to imagine such massive waves, like in my nightmare. Nervously I turn to Bri and decide to share my fear.

"I sometimes have nightmares about falling off a ship in a storm and sinking into deep water. I wake up scared and sweating. It makes me afraid of ever going into deep water."

Bri puts her arm around me. A wave of calmness washes over me again.

"I don't know ... you handled deep water pretty well today. You faced your fear as we went under the water to all the shipwreck sites, right?"

I smile. "I was so excited to see the shipwrecks, I forgot how afraid I was of deep water. Can we visit the *Edmund Fitzgerald*?"

"Not that ship," says Bri quietly. "It is still too recently a grave site, and only archaeological and scientific visits are allowed through the Canadian government."

I remember something. "Hey, on the drive here my dad was listening to a song, 'The Wreck of the *Edmund Fitzgerald*.' I didn't know it was about a real shipwreck!"

"It was a very sad day on Lake Superior," Bri says as she quickly wipes tears from her eyes.

"After the song was over, Dad was telling me how brave the crew was and how much respect people have for them. He said some believe the ship was hit by three waves in a row, called the Three Sisters. A nearby ship reported that. The wreck was discovered four days later."

"The people aboard were very brave!" Bri agrees. "It was just such a tragedy, and it wasn't just the *Fitz* that sank here. They say over 240 ships have been sunk or damaged near this same point."

"Speaking of Dad," I quickly say, "we should go check on him. I bet he's done with his lecture." ⚓

And Back Again

Bri nods and whoosh, we are back where we started in Duluth beside the shipwreck map in the Lake Superior Maritime Visitors Center.

I spot Dad down the hall packing up his stuff from his lecture.

"Hey, Chase!"

"Hey Dad! This is Bri."

"Who?" Dad looks puzzled. "Who's Bri?"

I laugh, "This is Bri ..." I say again, then notice she is nowhere to be seen. "She was just here. She knows a lot about shipwrecks. Bri? Bri where are you?"

I turn to my dad. "I want you to meet her, and I wanted to say good-bye."

I run around the corner and up the stairs, but still no Bri.

"Well, I hate to cut your search for Bri short," Dad says, "but we still have a long drive ahead of us."

Dad tells me we will stop at some of the maritime museums along the Upper Peninsula, like in Marquette and at Whitefish Point. I don't tell him that I've already seen them.

"Dad," I start quietly. "I don't think I've ever told you I was afraid of deep water. I have nightmares about it. That's why I never wanted to go diving."

"I didn't know you were afraid of deep water," he says. "I thought you just weren't interested in diving with me."

"I'd like to try diving now."

"You're not afraid anymore? How did you get over it?"

"I think it was looking at all those shipwrecks."

"Really? Looking at pictures of shipwrecks got you over your fear?"

"Something like that," I say with a smile. "Dad, after we finish with Lake Superior, where do we head next?"

"Lake Michigan."

"Well, then, Lake Michigan, here we come!"

As we head out of the museum, a statue tucked into a corner catches my eye.

"Dad!" I yell a little too loud. "Who's that?"

"Ah, you mean Brizo," he says as he nudges me with a smile. "Brizo was an ancient Greek goddess known as the protector of mariners, sailors and fishermen. She was also known for interpreting dreams."

I stare at the statue, which looks like Bri. As we walk past her on the way to the car, I swear she gives me a wink. ⚓

Glossary

AFT Towards the stern, or back, of a ship.

ANCHOR A heavy object attached to a rope or chain and used to hold the ship to the lake bottom.

ARCHIPELAGO A chain or group of islands.

BOW The front of a ship.

BREAKWALL A structure built for protecting a beach or harbor.

BUOY An anchored floating device used for navigation and sometimes to gather data.

CARGO Goods being moved by water, air or land, usually for commercial gain.

DISTRESS SIGNAL A signal from a ship that it is in danger.

FAIRLEAD A device used to guide a line (like in the photo on page 21).

FIGUREHEAD Generally a carved bust or full figure set at the very front of an old-fashioned sailing ship.

FORWARD Towards the bow, or front, of a ship.

FREIGHTER A ship designed to carry goods from one port to another.

GALE A very strong, sustained wind. The U.S. National Weather Service defines a gale as winds of 34 to 47 knots (63-87 kilometers per hour or 39-54 miles per hour).

GREEK GODDESS A female deity from ancient mythology.

GROUNDED When a ship is in water too shallow for it to float so it hits bottom. The number of feet a ship needs to float depends on the depth or **DRAFT** ship.

HARBOR A place on the coast or shore where a ship may find shelter or protection.

HAWSEPIPE The hawsepipe is the pipe through which the anchor chain travels. In maritime tradition "coming up through the hawsepipe" means working up from deckhand to officer.

HELMSMAN A person who steers a ship.

HULL The main body of a ship, including the bottom, sides and deck. It usually is made of wood or steel.

LEEWARD On or toward the side of a ship that is sheltered from the wind (**DOWNWIND**).

LEGEND A traditional story or myth.

LOCK A system used to raise and lower ships between two bodies of water at different heights.

MINESWEEPER A small warship designed to remove or detonate naval mines.

MARINER A sailor.

MARITIME Something connected to the sea or lakes, usually commercial or military.

MAST A tall upright post on a ship, generally carrying a sail or sails.

NAVIGATE Plan and direct the route or course of a ship by using instruments or maps.

PILOTHOUSE The part of the ship where the captain and navigators work, also sometimes called the **WHEELHOUSE**.

PORT The left side of a ship. You can remember it because "port" has the same number of letters as "left." A port is also a town or city where ships load, unload and "park."

PLUMB BOB A pointy tipped weight suspended a string to indicate a vertical line.

PRESERVATION Protecting or maintaining something, especially from loss, injury or danger.

PROPELLER A type of underwater fan connected to an engine that provides power for the ship to move.

PULLEY A grooved wheel used to raise or lower heavy items.

REEF A bar of rock, sand or a similar material, lying beneath the surface of the water.

SCHOONER A sailing ship with two or more masts and fore and aft (front and back) sails.

SCHOONER BARGE A type of ship with one or more sails and a flat bottom for carrying freight, often pulled by another ship.

SHOAL A natural underwater ridge or bar that rises near the surface of the water.

SONAR A system for detecting objects under water by using sound waves.

STARBOARD The right-hand side of a ship.

STEAMSHIP A ship that is propelled or moved by a steam engine.

STERN The back of a ship.

TELEGRAPH A ship's telegraph or **CHADBURN** used to signal direction and speed from the pilothouse to the engine room.

TUGBOAT A powerful boat used for towing larger boats, especially in a harbor.

WHALEBACK A particular style of cargo steamship, with a hull that curved above the waterline. When fully loaded, only the rounded portion of the hull could be seen above the waterline, resembling a whale in the water.

WINDLASS A mechanism for raising, lowering and holding an anchor.

WINDWARD On or toward the side of a ship from which the wind is coming (**UPWIND**).

YACHT A boat used for pleasure or sport. ⚓

'Chase' Our Maritime Heritage

Here's a few of the places Chase and his dad might go to give lectures or learn more about Lake Superior maritime history, starting from Minnesota and circling the lake. This list is not complete, so check visitor websites. (Some of the things Chase and Bri find in the museums – like a statue of Brizo – are not really there. But you'll find other cool stuff to explore.)

MINNESOTA
North Shore Commercial Fishing Museum, Tofte • commercialfishingmuseum.org • Opens seasonally to preserve and present an important part of shoreside history.

Split Rock Lighthouse, northeast of Two Harbors • mnhs.org/splitrock • One of the most photographed and visited spots in the state, with a drama-filled history and breathtaking views, operated by the Minnesota Historical Society.

Lighthouse B&B and Museum, Two Harbors • lighthousebb.org • The red brick lighthouse sits at Lighthouse Point near winding trails. It's also a B&B, operated by the Lake County Historical Society. Nearby is the *Edna G.* tug, available for viewing and tours.

***William A. Irvin* Museum Ship**, Duluth • DECC.org • This former U.S. Steel freighter is operated by the Duluth Entertainment Convention Center. Tours available in season.

Lake Superior Maritime Visitor Center, Duluth • LSMMA.com • Always free, this hands-on center operated by the U.S. Army Corps of Engineers in partnership with the Lake Superior Marine Museum Association is right beside the Duluth Aerial Lift Bridge.

Great Lakes Aquarium, Duluth • glaquarium.org • Find out more about our waters and waterways, plus touch a sturgeon in one of the many hands-on exhibits.

WISCONSIN
SS *Meteor* Museum Ship, Superior • superiorpublicmuseums.org • One of three

heritage sites under the care of the Superior Public Museums, this is the only example of a whaleback vessel still above water. Tours available seasonally at Barker's Island, which also has picnic spots, trails and a nearby marina.

Bayfield Maritime Museum, Bayfield • bayfieldmaritimemuseum.org • Seasonal with exhibits that interpret the nautical history of Bayfield and the Apostle Islands.

MICHIGAN
Ontonagon Lighthouse, Ontonagon • ontonagonmuseum.org • Owned and operated by the Ontonagon Historical Society, seasonal tours given of this beautiful restored lighthouse and keepers quarters.

Lighthouse Complex & Maritime Museum, Eagle Harbor • keweenawhistory.org • Run by the Keweenaw County Historical Society, the Eagle Harbor Lighthouse Complex features the old Life-saving Station, a Maritime Museum in the fog signal building, a Keweenaw History Museum, and a Commercial Fishing Museum in one of the assistant keeper buildings.

Marquette Maritime Museum & Marquette Harbor Lighthouse, Marquette • mqtmaritimemuseum.com • Three worthy sites: The Marquette Maritime Museum in its brownstone building, the red Marquette Harbor Lighthouse and the McClintock-Darter/Dace Memorial focused on a World War II submarine battle led by Marquette native Captain David McClintock.

Crisp Point Lighthouse, Luce County • crisppointlighthouse.org • This remote and stunning lighthouse right on the lakeshore is operated by the Crisp Point Light Historical Society. Open seasonally, you might also apply to be a volunteer lightkeeper there.

Great Lakes Shipwreck Museum, Whitefish Point • shipwreckmuseum.com • A multi-building complex with exhibits that include the *Edmund Fitzgerald* ship's bell, displays and videos about the U.S. Life-Saving Service, as well as Lake Superior's oldest operating lighthouse. It is operated seasonally by the Great Lakes Shipwreck Historical Society, which has its headquarters in a former historic National Weather Service building in Sault Ste. Marie.

Soo Locks Visitor Center, Sault Ste. Marie • lre.usace.army.mil (search Soo Locks Visitor Center) • Within the Soo Locks Park a great stop on the way to the viewing platform to watch boats passing through the locks. Exhibits focus on how locks work and information about the role of the U.S. Army Corps of Engineers on the Great Lakes, which also operates the center.

***Valley Camp* Museum Ship**, Sault Ste. Marie • saulthistoricsites.com/museum-ship-valley-camp • This more than 100-year-old former American Steamship Company freighter is operated by the Sault Historic Sites and features many exhibits, including two lifeboats from the *Edmund Fitzgerald* and an aquarium.

ONTARIO
***Alexander Henry* Museum Ship**, Thunder Bay • ltmstb.com/alexander-henry • A retired Canadian Coast Guard cutter, this ship is part of a blossoming collection of transportation-related exhibits being assembled by the Lakehead Transportation Museum Society. When fully gathered, it will have examples of water-, land- and air-borne transportation all connected to this region. ⚓

Ahoy, Resources

If this book has inspired you to look for additional resources, we'd like to suggest a few.

For teachers, Kathy Groth has developed a teaching guide that is a thematic planner covering all curricular areas for grades 3-8. To inquire contact her at grothkathy@yahoo.com.

The entire series of the Graveyard of the Great Lakes posters – one for each of the Great Lakes and the Outer Banks – can be purchased online through Lake Superior Gift Shop at LakeSuperior.com. Frameable or laminated wall maps of Lake Superior similar to that on pages 58-59, can be purchased online. You'll also find a number of shipwreck and maritime-related books for all ages and the Haunted Lakes series.

For additional information on diving and underwater preservation, we recommend viewing the Great Lakes Shipwreck Preservation Society's website at glsps.clubexpress.com. The National Park Service Junior Ranger program (nps.gov/kids/become-a-junior-ranger.htm) offers "underwater wonders" activity ideas.

For additional information about shipwrecks on Lake Superior, in addition to those listed in the maritime heritage pages, two of our favorite websites for additional photos and information are a collaborative effort of Wisconsin Sea Grant and the Wisconsin Historical Society at wisconsinships.org, and the Minnesota Historical Society's Historic Shipwrecks page at mnhs.org/places/nationalregister/shipwrecks. ⚓

Many Thanks!

Few things offer so much opportunity to say thanks as the writing of a book.

I want to thank my family for tirelessly reading and critiquing my earlier manuscripts; shipwreck historian Thom Holden, for reading my manuscript for accuracy; Donald Tubesing, founder of Whole Person Associates for reading my manuscript and offering additions; my young readers, Lyla Qualls and Max, Luke and Jack Yoder for the target audience feedback; and my son-in-law Kevin Raasch who tirelessly read and re-read all versions of the manuscript to help me keep it kid-focused. And to my husband, Chuck, for driving long distances and spending countless hours at maritime museums, always encouraging me.

Thanks to the staff from Lake Superior Publishing, including publishers Ron Brochu and Beth Bily plus Konnie LeMay and Siiri Branstrom for believing in me and my book from the very beginning.

The amazing historic and underwater photography featured within this book represents the extreme generosity of divers, historians, organizations, maritime collectors and others. My heartfelt thanks for the use of these images and please do take time to read the names of those on the photo credit pages. – *Kathy Groth*

An editor's special thank you to all of our final fact-checkers and others who lent aid: maritime historians Thom Holden and C. Patrick Labadie; Wisconsin maritime archaeologist Tamara Thomsen (who also owns Diversions Scuba in Madison); maritime history aficionado Brendon Baillod; diver Corey Daniel and BSA Venture Crew dive instructor Dean Soderbeck; wreck hunter Ken Merryman (who owns Superior Trips Scuba Charters); Bruce Lynn, executive director of the Great Lakes Shipwreck Historical Society; maritime historian Fred Stonehouse; and Brett Seymour, deputy chief of the Submerged Resources Center for the National Park Service – *Konnie LeMay*. ⚓

Big Lake

Lake Superior is the largest freshwater lake by surface area. It covers 31,700 sq. mi. or almost as much land area as the state of Maine.

Some of the oldest rocks on the planet can be found around Lake Superior – lava flows created these rocks 2.7 billion years ago.

Lake Superior holds as much water as all of the four other Great Lakes – Huron, Michigan, Ontario, Erie + 3 more Lake Eries.

Water within Lake Superior only leaves the system about every 200 years, while Lake Erie's water turns over every three years.

un Facts

People have lived along the shores of Lake Superior since it was formed after the glaciers left 10,000 years ago.

Lake Superior measures 350 miles east to west and 160 miles north to south. Driving around the lake is the same distance as Minnesota to Florida.

How Much Water in Lake Superior?

3 quadrillion gallons (3,000,000,000,000,000) or 10% of the World's Fresh Surface Water.

Images

Page 6-7 = Diver on the *America* by the National Park Service Submerged Resources Center.

Page 9 = Lake Superior Maritime Visitor Center in Duluth, courtesy U.S. Army Corps of Engineers • Marquette Lighthouse courtesy Marquette Maritime Museum • Whitefish Point Lighthouse courtesy Great Lakes Shipwreck Historical Society.

Page 10 = *Madeira* pilothouse by Tamara Thomsen • minesweepers from City of Thunder Bay Archives • telegraph on the *Gunilda* by Ken Merryman.

Page 11 = An illustration by Tanya Back based on the schooner *Dan Hayes* to show how the May Flower might look.

Page 12 & 13 = Lake Superior shipwreck map by *Lake Superior Magazine* • all underwater images and research vessel *Preservation* by Tamara Thomsen.

Page 14 = Old woodcut image from *The Graphic* newspaper courtesy the collection of Brendon Baillod.

Page 15 = Historic image of *Western Reserve* from the University of Wisconsin-Superior Lake Superior Maritime Collection.

Pages 16-17 = All underwater photos of the *Hudson* and the sonar graphic are from wreck hunters Kraig Smith, Bill Reynolds and Jerry Eliason • the wreck hunters pictured on page 17 are Ken Merryman, Kraig Smith, Jerry Eliason and Dan Fountain • the historic image of the *Hudson* at Houghton is from the collection of Brendon Baillod.

Page 18 = Top images by Tamara Thomsen • bottom image with diver by Ken Merryman.

Page 19 = Historic of the *Samuel P. Ely*, courtesy the St. Louis County Historical Society • diver by the *Ely*'s mast hole (circle on left) and by the *Ely*'s pump (circle on right) by Ken Merryman.

Page 21 = Historic postcard of the *Thomas Wilson*, courtesy collection of Marit Emilie Buseth • SS *Meteor* on display in Superior, Wisconsin, courtesy the Superior Public Museums • historic black-and-white image of the *Thomas Wilson* from the Elmer Engman collection • the fairlead by Ken Merryman • diver monitoring site by Jack Decker.

Pages 22-23 = All images from the Lake Superior Maritime Collection.

Page 24 = Young divers by Corey Daniel • other underwater images by Tamara Thomsen • photo of the *Edna G.* by Christian Dalbec of Friends of the *Edna G.* • historic image of *Madeira* courtesy Split Rock Lighthouse Historic Site.

Page 25 = Historic image of *Madeira* courtesy Split Rock Lighthouse Historic Site.

Page 26 = Images of Split Rock Lighthouse courtesy Split Rock Lighthouse Historic Site.

Page 27 = Split Rock Lighthouse by mkopka.

Pages 28-29 = Underwater photos courtesy Elmer Engman (the diver is Elmer Engman!) • historic images from the Lake Superior Maritime Collection.

Page 30 = Two newspapers reporting on the disappearance of the *Ira H. Owen* • historic image of *Ira H. Owen* & tug *Constitution* from the Lake Superior Maritime Collection • underwater images by Tamara Thomsen.

Page 33 = Marquette Lighthouse by Dale Fisher of the U.S. Army Corps of Engineers • underwater images by Tamara Thomsen (who is also in the "She took these!" photo).

Page 35 = Historic image of the *Bannockburn* in dry dock at Kingston, Ontario, on the Maritime History of the Great Lakes website.

Page 36 = All historic images from the City of Thunder Bay Archives showing building of ships from 1918-1919 at Canadian Car • map courtesy Michigan Technological University in Houghton.

Page 37 = R/V *David Boyd* courtesy the Great Lakes Shipwreck Historical Society.

Page 38 = Historic image from *Shipwrecks of Lake Superior* edited by James R. Marshall.

Page 39 = All underwater images by Ken Merryman.

Pages 40-41 = Gold Lifesaving Medals by Fred Stonehouse from *The Last Laker* • historic images from the Marquette Maritime Museum collection featured in *The Last Laker*.

Pages 42-45 = All images from the National Park Service and underwater images from the NPS Submerged Resources Center. (Diver on page 60 is of Brett Seymour, deputy chief of the Submerged Resources Center, with his underwater photo equipment.) Map on page 44 by *Lake Superior Magazine*.

Pages 46-47 = All images courtesy the National Park Service and underwater images from the NPS Submerged Resources Center.

Page 48 = *Edmund Fitzgerald* bell within the Great Lakes Shipwreck Museum courtesy the Great Lakes Shipwreck Historical Society • historic image of the *Edmund Fitzgerald* by Bob Campbell • graphic illustration by U.S. Army Corps of Engineers in the Lake Superior Maritime Visitor Center, Duluth.

Page 51 = photo illustration by Tanya Bäck. ⚓

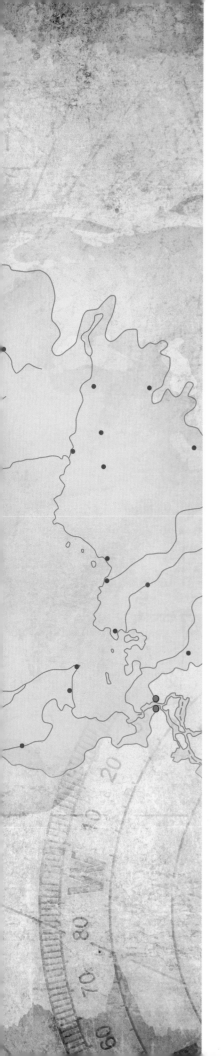

About the Author

Kathy (Ackley) Groth lives in Hayward, Wisconsin, with her husband, Chuck. They raised two daughters and now have five grandchildren she loves very much! Kathy enjoys the blessings of family and friends, gardening, reading, cooking, boating and traveling. Kathy's career in elementary education spans over 30 years. Her love for children and children's literature has always been her inspiration. The idea for *SUNKEN* was driven by Kathy's daughters who became interested in shipwrecks on a circle tour of Lake Superior when they were very young. After an exhaustive and unproductive search for children's books about shipwrecks, Kathy decided to write one. ... Twenty-eight years later the book is finished, and Kathy is proud to be able to present it to you. ⚓